Hello, Cat
You Need a Hat

by RITA GOLDEN GELMAN
Pictures by ERIC GURNEY

SCHOLASTIC INC.
New York Toronto London Auckland Sydney

ISBN 0-590-05793-6

Text copyright © 1979 by S & R Gelman Associates, Inc. Illustrations copyright © 1979 by Eric Gurney. All rights Reserved. Published by Scholastic Inc.

20 19 18 17 16 15   8 9/9

Printed in the U.S.A.   08

Hello, Cat
You Need a Hat

Oh, look.

Just look!

Your head is bare.

I have some hats that you can wear.

Come over here.

I'll give you some.

I have rain hats . . .

. . . hats for sun.

6

Hats for cold with fur and ear things.

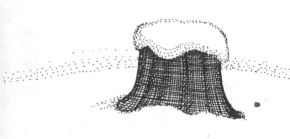

Walkie-talkie hats that
hear things.

9

Monkey hats for getting money.

Hats with nets for getting

honey.

If I wanted to, I would!

Try <u>this</u> hat.

You really should.

Hats to swim in.

Hats to hide in.

Hats to be a groom

and bride in.

You may have <u>this</u> hat.
You may.

I do not want it.
Go away!

Bands wear hats.
Police do, too.

Teams wear hats.
So why can't you?

Hats for cowboys.

Hats for knights.

Hats for welding.

Hats with lights.

Hats with chin things.

Hats with spin things.

Hats they give you when you win things.

I never spin.
I never win.
And I want nothing
on my chin.

TICKETS

19

Hats for crowning.

Hats for clowning.

Hats for cooking.

21

Bat hats.

Mouse hats.

Witch hats, too.

If witches wear them

WHY CAN'T YOU?

Firemen hats are best of all.

The way they make the water fall.

Have one.

Have one of your own.

**Get out of here.
Leave me alone!**

Have a helmet hat instead.

A helmet hat protects your head.

Can't you hear me?
NO! I said.

Astronauts wear hats in space.

Jockeys wear them in a race.

This one I know
will look
just right.

I think we're going
to have a fight.

Oh, no.

Don't fight.

I'll stop.

I will.

Come on.

We'll sit up on the hill.

Oh, look.

Just look!

Your feet are bare.

I have some shoes

that you can wear.

I'll give you some.

Come over here.